Mold Prevention Science

By   Clint S. Cooper   &   Larry Janesky

This book is dedicated to the hard-working men
and women at Basement Systems and CleanSpace®
dealerships worldwide, who solve mold problems
large and small for homeowners everyday.

Mold Prevention Science

by Clint Cooper and Larry Janesky
Design & layout by Wendy S. Vandersluis

Published by:
Basement Systems, Inc.
60 Silvermine Road
Seymour, CT 06483
1-800-640-1500
www.basementsystems.com

ISBN: 978-0-9776457-9-7

Contents

How To Use This Book

(A Reader's Guide)

There are seven brief chapters, each dealing with a specific aspect of mold and mold prevention (see table of contents). There are many photographs and sidebars to help you understand the ideas. The book outline progresses through logical steps to help the reader become familiar with the aspects of identification, investigation and ultimately the best solutions for your specific problems.

There are 8 different icons with different meanings:

Apples & Oranges

The two products discussed are very different.

Important!

This is important!

Additional information

This subject is very important in getting the results you want.

You will love the results from this!

CAUTION

Beware, don't make this mistake.

INSIDER INFORMATION

This is industry insider information.

Important for the resale value of your home.

Why We Wrote This Book

(A Joint Effort)

Clint Cooper and I teamed up to write this book, and we include the voices of many of us here at Basement Systems. In our businesses, many of the customers we meet are dealing with mold problems. Mold in the basement, in the crawl space, in the attic, and in walls, ceilings, and floors. Mold is a serious problem that can negatively affect health and property value. But most mold remediation contractors do not do anything to PREVENT mold from growing back by fixing the cause that made it grow in the first place. It is the intention of this book to educate you on the important issue about mold – preventing it.

Your local Basement Systems or CleanSpace® dealer may have given you this book. Otherwise, find your local Basement Systems or CleanSpace® dealer by calling 800-640-1500 or visit BasementSystems.com.

June 2013

Introduction

NOTE: This is not a do-it-yourself book because fixing a mold problem at your home is not a do-it-yourself project. It takes too much specialized knowledge, skill, and equipment-and it can be dangerous if you don't know what you are doing.

The purpose of this book is to give you enough information to make an educated decision on what work needs to be done in your home to prevent future mold growth .

What Makes Us Experts?

Experience.

We work every single day fixing moldy spaces that have water-damaged materials and loss of structural integrity. And, we have a team of coworkers and contributors who have been doing this for many years.

This book brings you the collective wisdom of literally thousands of contractors and tradesmen in the following professions –

Basement Waterproofing – (***Basement Systems, Inc.*** – 130 contractors throughout North America)

Crawl Space Retrofits – (***CleanSpace®*** – 165 contractors throughout North America)

Total Basement Finishing – (***Total Basement Finishing*** – 45 contractors throughout North America)

Home Energy Conservation – (***Dr. Energy Saver*** – 68 contractors in 33 states)

These teams includes experts in construction, repair, manufacturing, training and mold assessment, and installation of repair products. We have been working in homes like yours and taking responsibility for the results or our work. This book is the consensus of all of them - a truly valuable resource if your home or business has a "mold" problem, and needs repair.

Why Should I Fix My Mold Problem?

The problem will get worse. A mold problem grows bigger the longer you leave it alone. Mold germinates new mold "seeds" that get lifted by the air and redistributed all over a home, looking for new places to grow. The bigger the mold problem gets, the more it costs to fix.

Resale value. Who wants to buy a house with a mold problem? Nobody.

Your health could be at stake. Many people are sensitive to high concentrations of mold spores in the air. They react with allergy-like symptoms. Being exposed to high concentrations of mold spores for extended periods of time can cause sensitivity in some people where they were not allergic before. Some mold can produce toxins in the air that we breathe, which can cause reactions of the worst kind - even putting some people in the hospital!

Clean up without properly understanding and eliminating the cause is expensive, because the mold will only grow back again.

Mold in a home is not good for anyone. Evidence suggests that young children and the elderly are more susceptible, and no one benefits from poor air quality indoors.

CAUTION

Ultimately, the mold will end up ruining your home, your health and your family's well being.

You're Going to Pay for It Whether You Fix It or Not.

Consider this: We are all going to sell our homes one day. When we do, the buyer will hire a home inspector. This is something few people did 40 years ago, but now everyone does. In addition, when we list our home for sale, there is a disclosure form that sellers must fill out, explaining any defects with the house. These disclosure forms specifically ask about mold. You sign and swear to it, and the buyer gets a copy.

So it's simply unavoidable that the buyer is going to know about the mold problem in your home. Will they say "Aww shucks, don't you worry about that. We'll take the problem off your hands and deal with it ourselves." Not likely. In fact, they will probably walk away, and go look at the hundreds of other homes for sale out there.

If they do still want your home, they will either make you fix the mold problem before they buy it, or they will take the price of the repair off the price of the house. There is no escape.

Whether you get your mold problem and its cause fixed now and enjoy the piece of mind and healthy space for you and your family while you live there, or you don't, you are still going to pay for it. You'll pay and more later as the problem gets worse.

I don't know about you, but if I am going to pay for something whether I get it or not, I'm getting it now. *Make sense?*

Two Types of Mold Problems

 ## Mold Where You Can See It...

Visible mold - This is typically the fuzzy moss like growth people find on drywall, wood trim and wood framing or light mold growth on shoes in the closet. It is pretty easy to recognize, a little tough to clean up, and most important-difficult to understand how it got there in the first place. Regardless of color and smell, (sometimes a musty odor) mold can be dangerous. You should take caution and contact a professional who can help you decipher what is happening to cause visible mold growth in your home. If you think you have mold growing in your home and you can see it, you are probably right. Once it has grown large enough to be recognized visibly, a much more serious moisture issue exists somewhere in the building envelope. The solutions necessary to properly correct this type of mold will ALWAYS involve identifying the source of the problem – a leak, condensation or high relative humidity at the surface the mold is growing on.

② ... And Mold Where You Can't See It!

Invisible mold - Mold can be present in a home even when no visible growth signs are found, like in the typical dark wet areas (basements and crawl spaces.) In fact, mold is present long before it "grows" big enough to be seen by the naked eye. The invisible parts of the mold fungi are carried through the air like tiny dandelion seeds, landing on the surface of many potential food sources. The truth about mold's presence is a little surprising. It is a naturally occurring bio-organism, present throughout every environment we occupy. The invisible mold is actually the microscopic seed of the mold; unless the right conditions arise, we will never see it grow in our homes.

This wall looks fine on the finished side.

But when the paneling is removed, we find this!

Preventing Your Mold Problem is the 'Green' Alternative

We don't want to be guilty of 'greenwashing' here — when you make up some reasons why your product is environmentally responsible, but it's really a stretch to say as much.

However, here are a few valid points:
Rather than clean your mold problem with harsh chemicals, you could use a very labor intensive and expensive approach - replace the moldy building materials. Not to mention the fact that the mold will come back on the new material if the moisture problem that caused the mold isn't remedied to begin with. Preventing mold is the logical answer. Concrete is porous and lets water and moisture seep into your home. The remedy is making the environment dry, which prevents mold from growing in the first place.

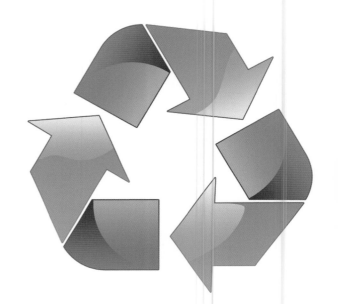

Mold in an attic.

Chapter 1

"Do I have a mold problem in my home?"

A lot of people ask this question.

They wonder if the black or green looking spots that show up in the bathtub or on the heating and cooling vents, are mold. Sometimes people are very sensitive to the musty smells from a basement or closet and wonder, "is that mold I smell?"

The internet is full of scary pictures of mold; men dressed in full protection white suits with respirators, walking around taking samples of the air. Common sense can help us arrive at some basic conclusions; but if you think you have a mold problem its best to seek professional help.

The biological facts are relatively simple to outline. If you invest your efforts in education and prevention, it is the least expensive route to take, and offers the most permanent solution available.

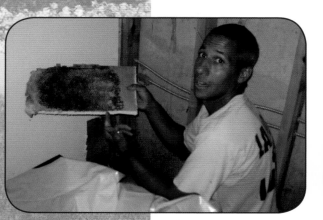

Moisture in your living space not properly taken care of will result in a mold problem.

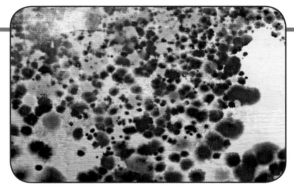

Mycotoxins are what some species of mold use to compete for space with other species – essentially waging chemical warfare on other molds.

Mold is a Living Organism

It breathes air, it consumes food, it requires water to survive, and fortunately, when you take one of these components away, it dies. Mold is a fungus, kind of like a mushroom, but a lot smaller (sometimes it can't even be seen with the naked eye.) It eats organic matter - anything that was once living – like plants and animals. Mold thrives in environments where we like to live - in structures made of organic material, like our homes. It likes temperatures between 32 and 100 degrees F, relative humidity (moisture in the air) between 70% and 99%, and is typically found in places that are damp or humid for extended stretches of time - like our basements and crawl spaces, for example.

INSIDER INFORMATION

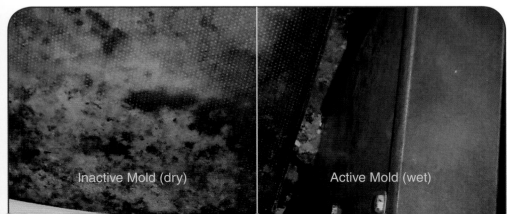

Inactive Mold (dry)   Active Mold (wet)

Active Mold!

'Active Mold' refers to Mold that is living and breathing. It's the mold that's growing and reproducing. It smells, and makes you itchy and uncomfortable. It can cause allergies and health issues especially in small children, and elderly family members.

Mold Grows?

When mold spores find the right combination of temperature, food source, and moisture - they grow. When mold grows it reproduces more airborne seeds to grow more mold. These seeds are like tiny parachutes that float through the air - just think of dandelion seeds in the wind. These seeds, called spores, are very light and the slightest breeze can lift them into the air, carrying the spores to new damp organic surfaces to grow on. If the spores stick to inorganic materials like clean metal, ceramic tile, porcelain, plastics etc, they will not grow. If they land on dry surfaces of any kind, they will not grow.

Some mold spores produce a chemical byproduct called mycotoxins. Mycotoxins are what some species of mold use to compete for space with other species – essentially waging chemical warfare on other molds. These compounds can affect our respiratory systems, even making us sick. You can't see the spores or the mycotoxins, but a lot of people can smell their musty signature.

Mold Can Go Dormant

When mold dries out it goes dormant. When it's dormant, it stops producing spores, and waits until the next period of high relative humidity or surface moisture to continue growing and producing spores again. When people have "reactions" to mold, they are not reacting to the mold on surfaces, but to elevated spore counts in the indoor air. It's the same as people who are allergic to pollen in the spring; they aren't reacting to the budding leaves of the trees but rather the airborne pollen that results from the trees budding.

Don't be fooled though. We cannot live a mold-free life! It is not natural for mold to be absent in our world. Mold is good – in the right places. Mold is the mechanism by which organic material is broken down in nature. Without mold, nothing that grew would break down and decay, ultimately feeding the next generation of plants and animals. But when we build a house out of organic materials (lumber, paper, plywood, cardboard, insulation, etc.), we don't want that material to rot back to the earth – we want our homes to last!

CAUTION

Beware of black mold!
Stachybotrys is a genus of molds, or asexually reproducing, filamentous fungi. Closely related to the genus Memnoniella, most Stachybotrys species inhabit materials rich in cellulose. The genus has a widespread distribution, and contains about 50 species.

The most infamous species, S. chartarum (also known as S. atra) and S. chlorohalonata are known as "black mold" or "toxic black mold" in the U.S. and are frequently associated with poor indoor air quality that arises after fungal growth on water-damaged building materials.

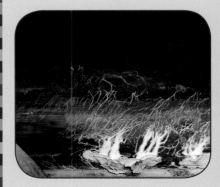

Chapter 2

The Modern Home?

These days there is more free information available online to the consumer, empowering us to be smarter with our time, money, and in this case our health. We have already established the fact that mold spores are present just about everywhere and that they can grow if we create environments where mold can thrive. Here is the key to living in a world where mold can show up just about anywhere - **prevention is the best solution to control all mold problems.**

Mold needs 4 things to grow.

1. Spores (seeds of mold)

2. Food (organic material)

3. Water or high humidity

4. Temperature between 32° and 100° F (0° and 43° Celsius)

We can't eliminate the organic material – our homes are made of it. We can't get out of the temperature zone – we like that zone ourselves! And we can't get away from the spores – they are everywhere (you're breathing some right now!) What we can control is the moisture – and therein lies our secret to mold prevention.

You can't find a doctor who says mold in a home is good. You can't find a doctor who says mold in your home is "not bad."
It's bad. It's all bad.
Besides irritating people with asthma and mold allergies, studies show that prolonged exposure to mold can actually cause asthma.

Mold = Bad

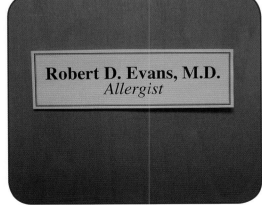

Robert D. Evans, M.D.
Allergist

The Modern Home

Continued

Q: Do we have more mold today than we did a hundred years ago?
Or do we just have higher standards and are more sensitive to mold?

A: The answer is *both.*

House in 1913

Apples & Oranges

House in 2013

Let's Talk About Some Rules of Building Science –

CAUTION

1 Moisture goes from more to less, and hot to cold.

2 Wood and organic materials are "hygroscopic" – meaning that when the air around them is damp, the materials absorb moisture out of the air and come into equilibrium with the moisture content in the air. When the air dries out, the materials dry out. That's easy to understand. Wet air, wet materials. Dry air, dry materials. It's okay for organic materials to get damp, so long as they can dry in a day or two before mold grows.

3 When you cool the air, you raise the Relative Humidity unless you take water out of it. In fact, for every one degree you cool it, you raise the Relative Humidity by approximately 2.2%.

Important!

"Relative" Humidity
Relative to What?

Relative Humidity (RH) is the amount of water in the air relative to the maximum amount of water the air can hold at that temperature.

If the air is 70 degrees and has a 60% RH, then the air is 60% full of water compared to the maximum amount of water 70 degree air can hold. The magic trick that keeps things interesting is that when you cool air, it shrinks and can't hold as much water. So if we cool the air without taking any water out of it, then the RH goes up, even though we have not added any water.

Picture this: You're holding a plastic water bottle that is 60% full. When you squeeze the bottle and make it smaller, the water level goes up. The opposite is true when we heat the air without adding water. The RH goes down. For every degree we cool the air, we raise the Relative Humidity by 2.2% provided we don't add or take any water out of it.

The Modern Home

Important!

Air Leaking OUT
⬅ causes air to leak in. ➡

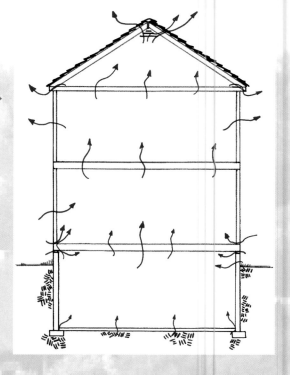

In homes built a hundred years ago, we had very leaky wall, ceiling and floor assemblies with no insulation. We had heat flow through the building envelope – inside to outside in the winter, and outside to inside in the summer. The house dried to the outside in the winter, as there were no vapor barriers, air barriers, or insulation preventing moisture from leaving the building. This was a good thing relative to preventing mold. Of course we were shivering in our homes and it took a great deal of energy to heat our homes (unevenly), but at least they could dry out.

Today's Home

Today we have homes that are much tighter. Are they "too tight"? Not hardly. In fact the average home has a long way to go before it's too tight. But we have to pay attention to how we build homes – where we put vapor barriers (they need to be on the warm side), what kind and how much insulation we install, and vent excess moisture outside (bath fans, clothes dryers, kitchen exhausts etc.)

ThermalDry Walls are vapor barriers.

We need to control our basements and crawl spaces from leaking obviously, and not allow air from the earth into our homes. We should not allow outside air into a below-ground space such as a crawl space or basement, because we will pay an energy penalty in the winter, and have high relative humidity and condensation in the summer time, causing mold.

TBF EverLast Walls are vapor barriers.

The Modern Home

Continued

One thing the modern home has today is air conditioning. This makes preventing mold more difficult? Why? A hundred years ago the way you (tried to) cool down was opening windows and maybe running a fan. We were not changing the temperature of the outside air as it came into the house, and therefore were not raising the relative humidity by "squeezing" the air to a cooler temperature. Today, when summer air leaks in, we cool it because the home is air conditioned. Air conditioning removes relative humidity, but not perfectly in all areas of the house. In fact, it creates cool surfaces such as ducts and wall surfaces, where the relative humidity is high and even up to 100% (condensation). All mold needs is relative humidity over 70% (The higher it is, the more different species of mold like it).

Another thing that is different these days is we are building homes from fast-growing farmed trees as opposed to old-growth trees. When you cut an old log you'll notice the darker inner core of the log, perhaps ¾ of the wood. This is "heartwood". The outer rings are lighter and called "sapwood". Sapwood has the sugary cellulose that mold loves to grow on – more so than heartwood. With today's fast-growing farmed trees, the trees may only be 30 years old when they harvest them and they are nearly all sapwood.

Fast-growing farmed trees are more susceptible to mold growth.

We also have lots of plumbing these days. More fixtures that use water means more chances for leaks. The water line to the ice maker on the refrigerator, dishwashers and the multiple bathrooms we have in modern homes are all more opportunities for leaks. All the other ingredients for mold are present.

The insurance industry top water damage claims are not from hurricanes, and floods, but leaks from pipes, water heaters, and washing machine hoses malfunctioning in the home.

Just Add Water!

Are we more sensitive to mold these days? Certainly our standards for health have gone up. We also spend a lot of time indoors compared to 100 years ago. By not being exposed to outdoor mold spores as much, we may not have built up a resistance or immunity to mold spores and pollen. There was no Claritin in 1900!

Today's drug industry is a thriving business. The doctor's never ask you, "What's going in the home?"

Continued

Can you clean mold with bleach?

Important!

The problem with bleach...

A lot of people think that mold is no big deal, they have seen it all their lives in bathrooms or basements, they just use bleach to clean it up and forget about it. Did you ever wonder why it keeps coming back in the places where it was removed? Now at least you know that if the area is wet or damp in those places it will encourage mold to return, but did you know that bleach actually feeds the mold you thought you were cleaning? In high school you may have taken a chemistry class, and on the molecular level they would have discussed compounds like nitrates. Tiny little traces of these compounds are left behind when Sodium Hypochlorite (Bleach) is applied to a surface. These compounds are fertilizer for the next group of molds to land there!

The water in the hypochlorite penetrates below the surface of porous materials like wood framing, while the bleach is left on the surface and eventually gases off into the atmosphere. The root of the mold fungus is left below the surface and regenerates again over time.

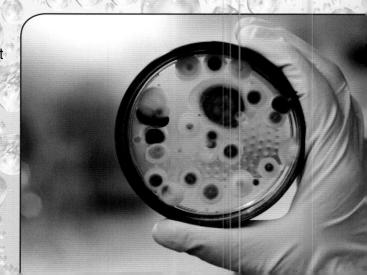

The Risks of Cleaning it Yourself ?

CAUTION

The problem with do-it-yourself...

Do-it-yourself projects are popular, with national big box stores offering the materials and advice for home repair and improvement. There are certainly many books available by experts to walk a homeowner through small-one-hour projects to ambitious multi-person remodels. There are of course a wide variety of professional service companies also marketing their talents for hire. Indeed, some work should be left to professionals, such as when permits must be pulled for electrical work.

Mold removal, testing, and prevention should all be left to professionals licensed in this work, equipped to protect themselves and homeowners from the potential hazards mold can present.

Professionals should be licensed in the particular service they are offering to you, and your home. A written contract should always spell out what services or products you are purchasing, any warranties they are offering, and what standards determine the success of a project.

Chapter 3

The Secret to Success is Moisture Control

CAUTION

Preventing mold involves controlling molds' signature element to survival - water. The water we are referring to can be a little tricky to understand. There are two forms of water that mold can access in order to survive. The first example is visible water, like in a wet basement or the leak in a plumbing pipe. The second form of water is vapor in the air. It's called Relative Humidity. This is a measure of how much water is in the air compared to the maximum amount of water the air can hold AT THAT TEMPERATURE. There are two ways to increase the Relative Humidity – cool the air, or add water to it. There are two ways to reduce the Relative Humidity – heat the air or take water out of it (dehumidify).

Sources of Moisture in a Home

Plumbing leaks

Vapor Transmission

Condensation

Groundwater leakage

Wicking

Plumbing Leaks

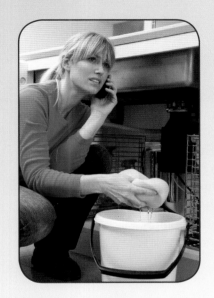

Let's begin with the most obvious water problem, plumbing leaks. If your house is on a slab foundation, some plumbing is likely located in the sub floor of your home. It was put in place before the concrete was poured, and the walls were built. If you have a leak in this plumbing, it is typically shows itself where the piping comes up out of the floor and ends at a sink or a toilet. Sometimes a slow leak can go undetected here, especially under a sink where cleaning supplies and towels may be blocking the view of the plumbing directly. Without a monitoring system present 24 hours a day, no one would remember to be "watching" out for leaks, much less alert you to this potential. Remember, water and organic material mixing, is the perfect recipe for mold growth. An alarm, such as a WaterWatch alarm, can be placed on the floor in these areas to signal you (just like a smoke alarm) if a leak begins, and give you plenty of opportunity to address a short-term water problem, before it turns into a mold problem. This same tool is used in your water heater overflow tray; it acts as a watch guard for the home, instantly alerting the owner to any new leaks that have started.

Flood*Ring*®
Water Tank Protection System

The FloodRing will protect your home from a water heater leak and give you time to fix it before it becomes a real problem.

WaterWatch® Alarm System

The WaterWatch alarm will signal you of an unforeseen water leak from plumbing.

Moisture Control

INSIDER INFORMATION

Detecting Moisture

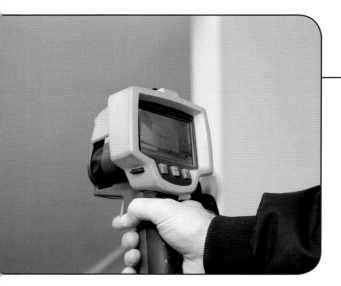

Experienced inspectors will have access to a host of moisture detection tools to identify moisture problems that give life to mold. Evaluating the moisture levels on surfaces, underneath carpet, and in some cases behind drywall, without the need to tear out materials and disrupt the homes' finished look. Thermal imaging technology is an amazing advance in leak detection, making the otherwise invisible, visible! The better the inspectors diagnostic tools and knowledge, the less cost and disruption to your home is necessary to fix and prevent mold problems.

Prevention is the key. When we control the moisture, we control the mold.

The more difficult form of moisture to control in an indoor environment is certainly relative humidity. This particular form of water is not as readily noticeable to you because it's invisible! This water vapor in the air, floats throughout our homes undetectable to the human eye. A measuring device called a hygrometer is used to detect the levels of humidity in the air. Most molds are able to grow when the relative humidity climbs above 70%.

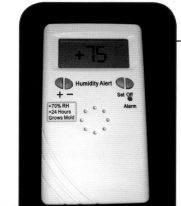

Digital Hygrometer

Traditional Hygrometer

Moisture Control

Detecting Moisture

Important!

Here's an important point. Mold doesn't grow in the air in the center of a room. It grows on surfaces. So it doesn't matter what the relative humidity is in the air in the center of the room – it only matters what the relative humidity is on the surface of your wall / ceiling / organic building material. We said that if we cool the air by one degree without taking water out we raise the relative humidity by 2.2%. So if we had a 60% RH in our room air, but the surface was 10 degrees cooler, when that air touches it the RH will go up to 22% - enough for mold to grow. Keeping cold surfaces insulated to prevent mold growth is often part of prevention.

Mold growth on painted drywall.

Insulating pipes will help prevent condensation.

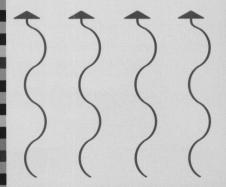

Moisture Control

Air Conditioners

Cooling systems are designed to remove humidity as a consequence of cooling the air. However a common problem in today's homes is that the cooling system is oversized. Yes oversized, not undersized. If the cooling system cools the air rapidly and satisfies the thermostat and shuts off, then it won't run long enough to take enough water out of the air to keep the relative humidity under control. Your cooling system should run continuously on a hot summer afternoon. If it turns on and off at the most peak cooling hours a hot summer day, it's oversized. If the total run time is 40 minutes per hour, then it's 33% oversized and not able to run enough to dehumidify the air. If you turn your thermostat down, it will reduce the temperature too much and you'll feel cold and clammy.

Oversized air conditioners don't run enough to remove moisture from the air.

Moisture Control

Basements & Crawl Spaces

The places that have the highest relative humidity in your home in the summer are the basement and crawl space. This is because the outside air was cooled without taking any water out of it like the air conditioning system does (well or not) upstairs. The basement or crawl space is in the cool earth and it's cool, and therefore cools any summer air that enters it. You can't use the air conditioning system to dehumidify the air in a basement or crawl space because the air is already cool!

Crawl Spaces are cold and damp environments, a perfect place for mold to grow!

The mold is fed a constant source of moisture you never even knew was there!

Moisture Control

Dehumidifiers

Apples & Oranges

A dehumidifier cools the air to get the water out of it, but puts the heat back into the air in the room – so it doesn't cool the space. But most dehumidifiers are designed to operate in warm temperatures. In fact they are tested in a chamber at 80 degrees. It's easy to dehumidify air that is 80 degrees because it's 48 degrees over freezing (the most you can cool the air before it freezes of course).

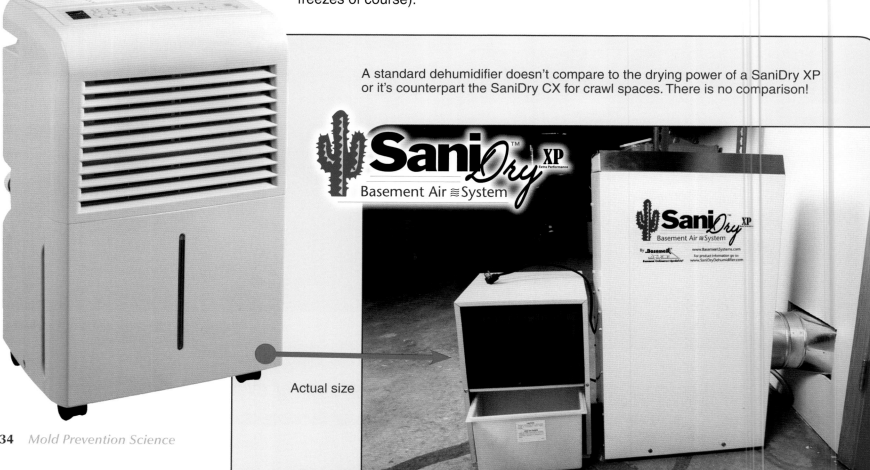

A standard dehumidifier doesn't compare to the drying power of a SaniDry XP or it's counterpart the SaniDry CX for crawl spaces. There is no comparison!

Actual size

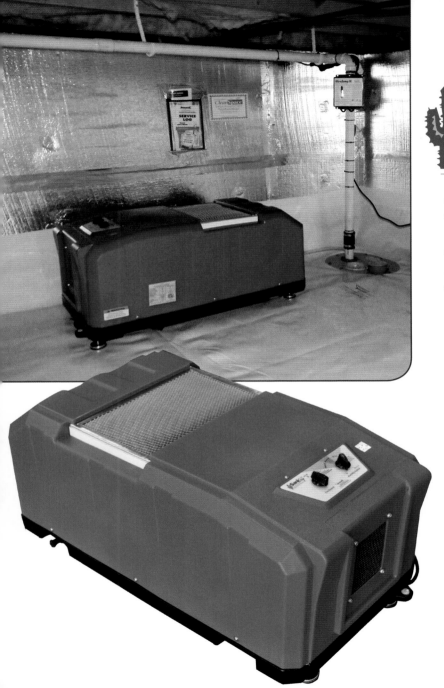

SaniDry CX
Crawl Space and Basement Air ≋ System

Crawl space and basement temperatures may be in the low 60's, and a lot closer to freezing. Few dehumidifiers are designed to work well at these lower temperatures. The "SaniDry Basement Air System" and the "SaniDry CX Crawl Space Air System" dehumidifiers are designed to work at these temperatures. Many other features such as a heat exchanger, large blower, and specially designed refrigeration system and controls make them about 10 times more efficient at getting water out of the air as a standard household dehumidifier that homeowners are used to seeing. Further, they remove water at about 3.3 cents of electricity per pint of water removed compared to 11 cents for a standard household model. **They work!**

How does it perform so incredibly well with the same amount of energy that less-effective 20-pound-weakling dehumidifiers use?

1. The SaniDry XP blows air over a huge cold coil. It looks like a truck radiator instead of the little squirrelly spiral coil of dinky dehumidifiers.

2. The SaniDry XP runs the exiting dry, cold air through a special heat-exchange core that pre-cools the incoming wet air and recaptures energy.

3. The SaniDry XP's powerful 250 cfm blower not only grabs more air in to dry faster, but moves the dry air out around your basement to dry the contents of your basement.

There are other component reasons SaniDry XP wins the dehumidifier battle, but these are the main ones.

Chapter 4

The Quality of Our Indoor Air

How do you know if the air in your home is safe?

Government agencies and medical sites have created many articles addressing exposure to too much mold, the certain types of mold that should be avoided, and when to call in a professional. With all of this data, there is surprisingly not one mention of a numerically safe level of mold a person or home can be in contact with. The guidelines for mold cleanup and safe exposure level are essentially unstated. The answers are often left to the opinion of the individual contractor. This does not mean that a professional does not follow protocols, or focus on the most stringent tests to verify effective mold removal. The indoor air quality industry has created a vast system of certifications in testing, and remediation. This is done in an effort to create standards and quality control benchmarks or safety protocols to measure successful remediation. Basically, a professional will tell you the types of mold measured and the amounts found should be lower inside the building, than a sample of the outside air.

INSIDER INFORMATION

Technology Fact Sheet

AIR SEALING

Seal air leaks and save energy!

WHAT IS AIR LEAKAGE?
Ventilation is fresh air that enters a house in a ... excess moisture

noise, dust, and the entry of pollutants, insects, and rodents. Reducing infiltration can signifi-cantly cut annual heating and cooling costs, ... durability, and create a

Indoor Air Quality

Fundamental Problems

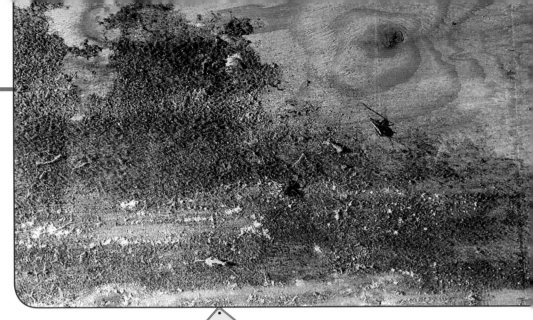

This book has focused primarily on causation, - what allowed the mold to show up in the first place. This is so important in understanding the fundamental problems associated with EVERY mold problem. The mold never shows up where it cannot survive, it requires a host environment that feeds the mold all three key ingredients. We cannot escape the reality of mold showing up wherever we live, it likes the same habitats, the same temperatures, and moisture that we do. Unfortunately, when allowed to thrive in our habitats it alters the quality of the air we breathe, it can cause us irritation affecting our health and happiness.

37

Indoor Air Quality

Fundamental Problems

It is easier to heat, cool, and clean the same air over and over again. This basic understanding of how air flows inside of a building helps us deduce the simplest way to "clean the air up." Simply find the focal point of all the air movement, in this case, the central heating and air system located in a closet or attic, and clean it! All the air in the building runs through the air handler unit, is heated or cooled, and sent throughout the home in the duct work, and recycled back to the return box again.

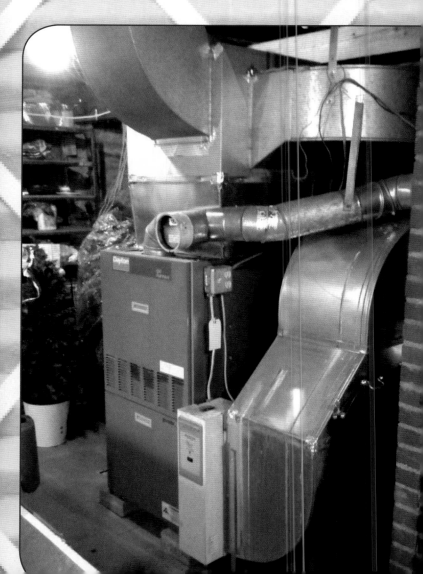

Dirty air conditioning coil from not changing filters, and not servicing the system annually causes mold to grow in your duct work!

Fundamental Problems

While mold doesn't grow on CLEAN metal, the evaporator (cold air conditioning) coil inside the air handler can be dirty, and probably is. Condensation keeps the dirt wet and mold can grow on it. The spores this mold produces are released into the duct system and distributed throughout the house. One Orlando Florida homeowner told us that after discovering the mold in her air handler, the Dr. Energy Saver contractor got rid of it as part of a variety of improvements she had done. The results were miraculous to her. Her daughter, who had allergies, was literally taken off the allergy medicine!

Change your furnace filter often. This home owner didn't, resulting in dust getting through onto the heating and air conditioning equipment, and inside the ducts.

Close-up on condensation.

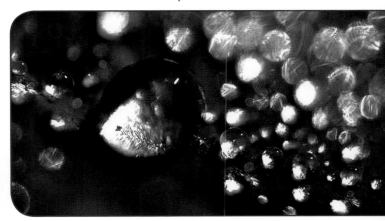

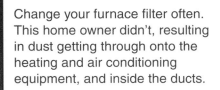

Condensation keeps the dirt (dust) wet and mold can grow on it.

Indoor Air Quality

Fundamental Problems

We find it interesting and unfortunate that doctors don't ask about what is going on in allergy sufferers' homes. Doctor's don't suggest having ducts, crawl spaces, basements and attics inspected by a professional to make sure they aren't just treating the symptoms rather than removing the cause. People live in homes that are making them sick and are unaware of the cause. This is more common than most of us think.

A vital part to any set of solutions your contractor shows you should include methods to reduce indoor air contaminants. Filtering the air we circulate in our home makes sense. Effective filtration should "catch" the microscopic particulates - like mold spores. Placing those filters/mechanisms in areas more likely to have higher spore counts makes the best sense. Of course you know by now it is not enough to react to airborne mold spores, you must prevent mold from growing in the first place!

SaniDry XP not only dehumidifies your home but also removes toxic mold spores and conditions the air you breath.

Fundamental Problems

The SaniDry air systems previously mentioned not only dehumidify the air; they also have particulate filtration. They will remove particles out of the air down to 2 microns in size – and all mold spores are bigger than that.

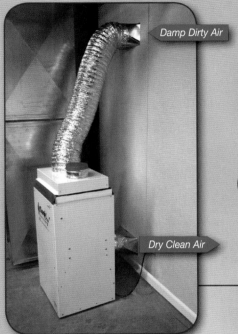

Damp Dirty Air

Dry Clean Air

Your unfinished area with SaniDry™XP ducted through the TBF Partition Wall.

A SaniDry™XP Basement Air System installed in the unfinished area, ducting dry filtered air into a beautiful finished TBF basement.

Damp Dirty Air Out!

Dry Clean Air In!

A finished basement with the SaniDry located in the unfinished area.

*A note here about stand alone air purifiers: There are many devices available today for purchase which claim to "kill" airborne contaminates. Assuming they do what they are claiming to do, purify the air, it does beg a basic question. How much air are they cleaning? Likely the few feet closest to the units themselves and not much more. So you need several for each room of your house? Make sure to check the rated area of effectiveness for each unit. It would be a shame to have an effective cleaning device that only worked in a 5' sphere of influence, right?

Chapter 5

Use Inorganic Materials in Wet Spaces

What are organic materials?

Organic materials are any material that was alive at one time – primarily trees, but there are also cotton, latex (rubber) and leather contents in your home too. Where we find drywall, wall coverings, paint, trim carpentry, carpet and flooring materials, we can assume all these to be organic based. When organic materials get wet, bad things happen like mold and rot.

It's not a new idea to use inorganic materials in places that get wet. We don't have wooden bath tiles for example, and our sinks aren't made from lumber or shower doors from plywood. In places like kitchens, and bathrooms we use ceramic, porcelain, stainless steel, and Formica.

Wet Spaces

Inorganic Materials

The insurance industry spends millions of dollars a year replacing wet damaged materials that become infected with mold, creating unsafe environments to live in. If you have a water "incursion" i.e. a water heater leak, a leaking pipe, a ground water leak, or any number of other problems, you call your insurance agent for help right? He sends an estimator out to the property to evaluate the extent of the damage and hopefully your policy pays for the necessary repairs.

But in most cases the damaged materials are replaced with the same vulnerable organic materials - and will be ruined again with another leak in the future.

Wet Spaces

Prevention is the key: Monitor likely problem areas and protect yourself from mold growth by using inorganic materials.

In places like basements and crawl spaces, which can be wet from a groundwater leak or a plumbing leak, or have high relative humidity, we can use plastic, foam insulation instead of fiberglass, cement board, and vinyl. In fact, a system called Total Basement Finishing, beautifully finishes basement with all inorganic materials. Literally if there were a foot of water in a basement, you just pump it out, dry it out and nothing is ruined and there is nothing for mold to grow on!

Wet Spaces

Inorganic Materials

Crawl spaces are great places for mold to grow. The problem is they are vented – which is an energy waste in the winter, and causes high humidity and condensation in the summer. If the floor is dirt, which most are, the steady invisible stream of water vapor coming up from the earth is another problem. A book by Larry Janesky called *"Crawl Space Science"* explains all the problems in complete detail. Of course, it provides solutions too. The "CleanSpace" crawl space encapsulation system and all its accessory strategies such as the SmartSump, SmartDrain, SilverGlo wall insulation, and SaniDry Crawl space air system will transform your crawl space into a place where mold doesn't stand a chance!

Moisture from the ground underneath a crawl space keeps wood damp, creating and ideal location for mold to grow.

SilverGlo insulation being installed to insulate a cold, damp crawl space, making the home more comfortable and reducing condensation.

CleanSpace®
Crawl Space Encapsulation System®

Mold shows up in any home where the perfect environments conducive to growth are created. It only makes sense to address these areas first, and to equip yourself with knowledge, in the long run you will be a smarter consumer.

CASE STUDY

Project: Smith Residence
Location: Collinsville IL
Date: December 2012

Mold Before

PROBLEM

The home was built in 1975 in a suburban setting in Collinsville Illinois. In 1995, the homeowners decided to add living space to the rear of the main structure. The exterior of the addition was constructed of brick and was supported by a poured concrete foundation. Approximately thirteen years after construction, the homeowners began to notice mold in the basement.

Remedy After

SOLUTION

Woods Basement Systems went into the home and gave a thorough inspection of the mold problem. They agreed upon a solution and set an appointment for work to be completed. Woods went in and removed all the moldy material, cut back the walls, and applied Mold X Neutralizer to clean the remaining mold. Woods then permanently waterproofed the basement, installed an EverLast Wall System, and a SaniDry XP air system, in the basement.

Mold Before

RESULTS

The installation by Woods Basement Systems was extremely effective. Not only was the mold gone, the basement did not leak anymore in heavy rains. The basement was now finished with inorganic materials which cannot be ruined in the event of a future plumbing leak. The air was clean, dry, and healthy.

PROJECT SUMMARY

Installing Contractor: Woods Basement Systems
Products Installed: (2) SaniDry XP, TBF EverLast Wall System, ThermalDry Flooring

Remedy After

Mold Before

Remedy After

Mold Before

Remedy After

Project: Angfang Residence
Location: Scarsdale, NY
Date: June 6th 2013

PROBLEM

The homeowner smelled mold in their home. The basement was finished by the previous owner many years ago and needed to be re-done. Several plumbing leaks and a window well flooding had wet the basement multiple times over the last ten years.

SOLUTION

Connecticut Basement Systems was called for a solution. Upon removal of the paneling, the mold was found inside the wall on the drywall and wood studs. All the old walls were removed. All the wood, drywall, and fiberglass insulation in the basement was eliminated. The Total Basement Finishing System was installed using cement board, vinyl finished foam insulation, and plastic trim. No paint was used. All materials are mold resistant inorganic materials that will survive a flood unharmed.

RESULTS

A beautiful finished basement, with a warm dry living space, and clean healthy air. A space where mold won't grow in the event of a plumbing or other leak.

PROJECT SUMMARY

Installing Contractor: Connecticut Basement Systems – Tibor Mrmus, Senior Installer.
Products Installed: (2) SaniDry XP, TBF EverLast Walls, ThermalDry Flooring, Ceilings Tiles.

TBF Total BASEMENT Finishing
From Basement to Beautiful!™

Chapter 6

The Lesson is Prevention...

A lot less than cleaning mold up again and again

If you have mold, even if you have it professionally remediated, you need to fix the moisture problem so the mold doesn't grow back. So the first part, is fixing the moisture problem. If the mold dries out it goes dormant and stops producing spores. If you want to take the next step and remove the "dormant/dead bodies" of the mold, contact an experienced mold remediation contractor.

Mold -X neutrailizes mold.

Of course, the contractor that gave you this book likely will be able to help you with preventing mold in parts of your home. Some contractors specialize in preventing mold in crawl spaces, and some in crawl spaces and basements.

Others can help you with spaces such as an attic or with mold inside an air handler – you can find them at **DrEnergySaver.com or call them at: 877-479-3637**.

Chapter 7

What to do now?

To get your mold problem fixed correctly, you'll need to know exactly why the problem showed up in the first place. Finding this out is simple-contact your local Basement Systems or CleanSpace® dealer if you haven't already. You can find your local dealer by visiting **www.BasementSystems.com**

You can expect a qualified professional to come out to your home for a complete inspection, consultation, and a free written proposal including cost. Then you can have the work completed and feel great knowing your home has been equipped to prevent the most likely mold problems from happening again.

Mold must be prevented to have a healthy home for your family!

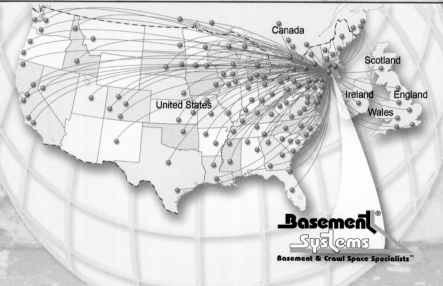

Canada

Scotland

Ireland England

United States

Wales

We're There. The Basement Systems dealer network spans North America, the United Kingdom, and Ireland.

Basement
Systems
Basement & Crawl Space Specialists™

Remember, you are going to spend more if you don't <u>fix the mold</u>!

Now you've read the very latest, cutting-edge '*Mold Prevention Science*.' You are an educated consumer and know what to do. Your local Basement Systems dealer can help you with the items discussed in this book because we know all of this stuff and live it everyday.

Basement Systems National Headquarters
800-640-1500

About the Authors

Clint Cooper has been involved in the mold remediation and mold prevention industry with his local community in Memphis, Tennessee since 2007. He currently owns the Redeemers Group, a full service basement waterproofing, crawl space repair and foundation recovery business and partners with the Basement Systems international team. Clint graduated from Middle Tennessee State University with a degree in Agricultural Business with an emphasis in organizational communications. He was a member of the Phi Theta Cappa honor society.

His passion for education has led him to become certified in residential and commercial mold testing and remediating. He is recognized by the state of Tennessee to conduct continuing education credits for realtors, home inspectors and code enforcement personnel for crawl space repair and foundation repair. He currently teaches these classes in Memphis every quarter and is working with the state of Mississippi towards reciprocity credits for similar professional networks.

He was raised on a rural working cattle farm in Middle Tennessee and was actively involved in the Boy Scouts of America where he obtained his Eagle Scout rank. In college he also served in the United States Marine Corps infantry. He was honored to serve his county in Fallujah, Iraq in 2004 as part of Operation Iraqi Freedom II.

Clint currently lives in Fayette County with his wife Amy and their two daughters Kaelyn and Addison. When he is not working he enjoys time spent outdoors with friends and family. He is involved in his local church, Fellowship Memphis and volunteers as a mentor with the Warriors Circle, a nonprofit organization for recovering addicts.

Larry Janesky is an authority on basement repair and building effective businesses that serve homeowners well. In 1982 he began five years of self employment as a carpenter and builder before founding Basement Systems Inc. in 1987. Today, Basement Systems is the largest network of waterproofing and crawl space repair contractors in the world. Larry has taken personal responsibility for repairing 34,000 basements over 24 years through his local installation business in Connecticut. Larry is also president of Total Basement Finishing, a leading network of finishing contractors, and Dr. Energy Saver, a network of energy conservation contractors.

Along with his friend Greg Thrasher, Larry co-founded Foundation Supportworks in Omaha, Nebraska. Larry has trained thousands of talented, dedicated basement repair contractors and their employees in the last 20 years. He holds 29 patents.

Larry is the author of 7 books including 'Dry Basement Science', 'Crawl Space Science', 'Basement Finishing Science', 'Home Comfort Science', and 'The Highest Calling – An Inspirational Novel About Business and Life, Struggle and Success.' He writes a daily blog called 'Think Daily', received by over 7000 people each morning. Like Clint, Larry is also an Eagle Scout.

Larry enjoys seeing everyone around him succeed. His mission is to make the world a better place for homeowners, employees, businesspeople and society in general, by helping build successful businesses that serve all effectively.

He lives in Middlebury, Connecticut with his wife Wendy, his son Tanner, and daughters Chloe and Autumn. He enjoys outdoor activities with his family and is a passionate motocross rider.

Acknowledgements

We would like to acknowledge the following people
and companies for their contributions:

Our spouses and children who allow us to share our
work, stories and experiences with them.

Connecticut Basement Systems,
Redeemers Group,
Woods Basement Systems

Wendy Vandersluis for layout and design.

The staff at Basement Systems, Inc., CleanSpace®,
Total Basement Finishing, Dr. Energy Saver, and our
many dealers who are helping to make the world a
better place by fixing mold problems every day.

Trusted Partners

Basement Systems consist of 5 sister companies within an expansive network. All companies are industry leaders in their respective fields. Much like *Mold Prevention Science*, each has developed an informational book about problems homeowners face and their options for solutions. Visit their websites and request a free copy of their books, compliments of our network.

Basement Systems®, Inc.
Basement waterproofing

BasementSystems.com

Dry Basement Science
What to Have Done... and Why

CleanSpace®
Crawl space repair

CleanSpaceSystem.com

Crawl Space Science
What to Have Done... and Why

Total Basement Finishing™
Basement finishing

TotalBasementFinishing.com

Basement Finishing Science
What to Have Done... and Why

Dr. Energy Saver™
Home energy contracting

DrEnergySaver.com

Home Comfort Science
What to Have Done... and Why

Foundation SupportWorks™
Structural repair

FoundationSupportWorks.com

Foundation Repair Science
What to Have Done... and Why

Notes